Learning to Surf

Written and Illustrated by Jason Cole

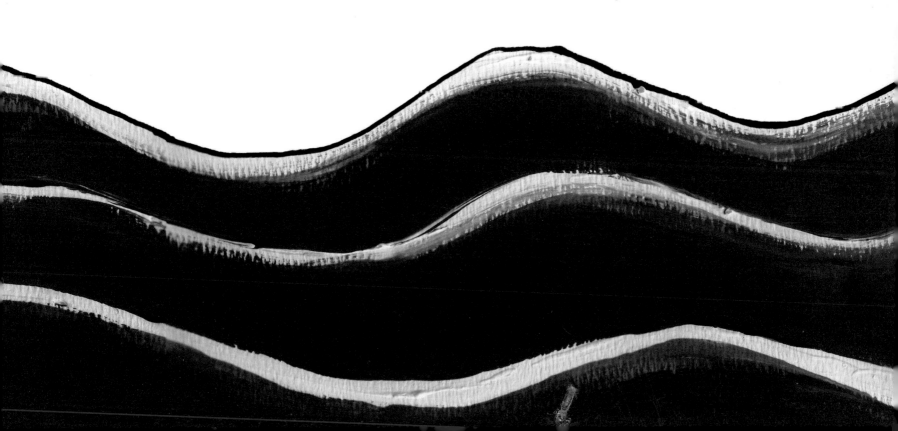

Last summer, I stayed at my Gran's. She has a house by the sea. That was the summer that I learnt to surf.

My Dad gave me his old surfboard so I jumped right in. The waves were quite big so I jumped right out again.

My sister gave me some advice. "Balance" she said, "Surfing is all about balance." So with this in mind, I tried again.

Her advice was not as useful as I thought. The only time that I was balanced was when I was on the beach.

Stella gave me
some good advice.
"Don't bring any of that
sand into this house or you
won't be able to
sit for a week!"
I took it.

My brother said
that it's all in your diet.
But I found that hard to
believe, judging from
what he puts
into his
stomach.

I should have had a lighter lunch, because I spent the next day at the bottom of the sea.

"Try, try and try again" said my Gran. "It will come in time. A little patience will go a long way."

Try,......try...

...and try again.

I decided to take it slowly and spend the next day snorkelling. You can learn a lot about the ocean when you're under it.

The next day I stood up and to my Surprise, I stayed up. Balance, eating right and patience did the trick. I was surfing.

Now I surf almost every day and I love it. Some day I will win a surfing trophy. All of my hard work has paid off.

Maybe next summer I will teach my little sister how to surf. She thinks that she already can.

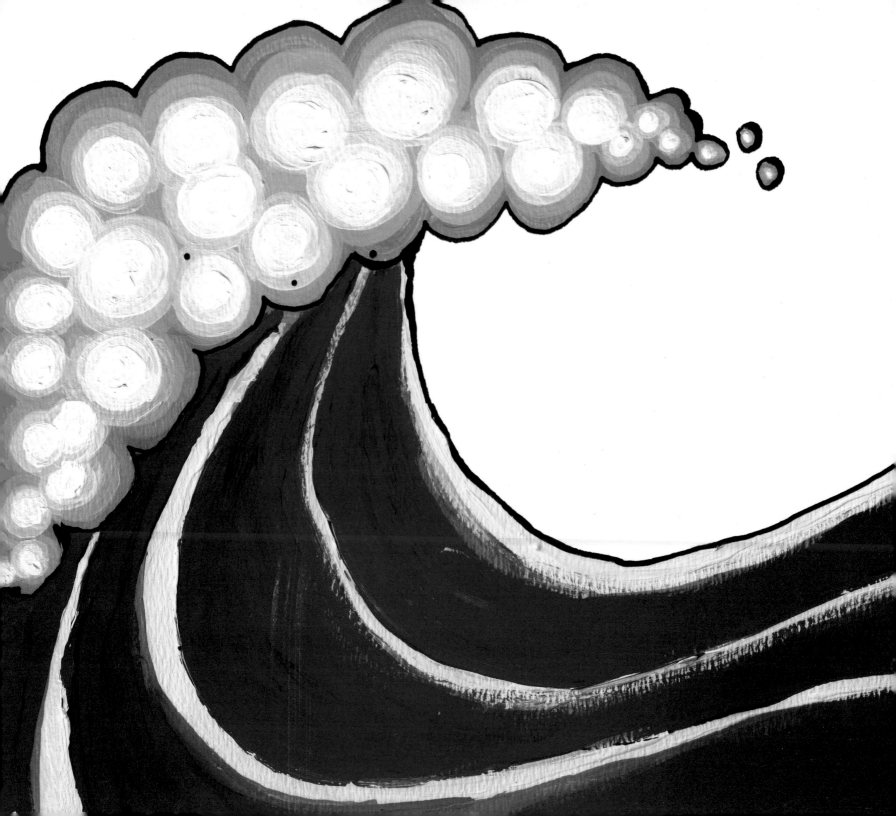

The End

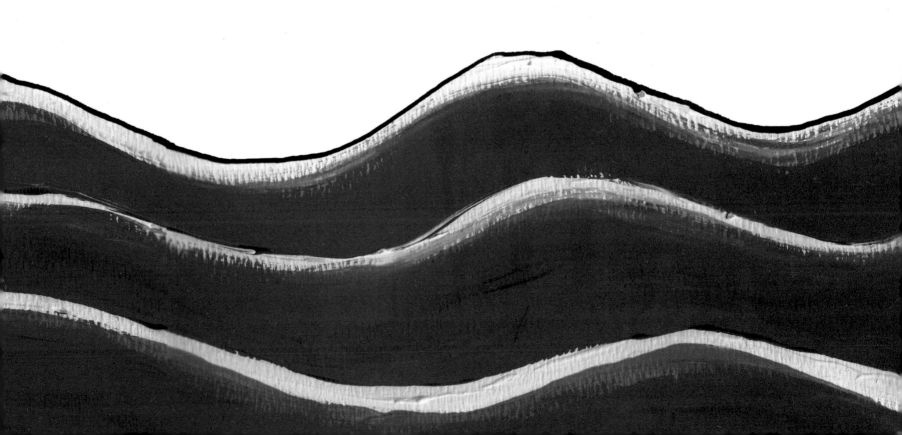

Learning something new can be difficult. But with a little advice and a lot of practice you are sure to have the time of your life.